MEZOLITH

MEZOLITH

STORY
BEN HAGGARTY

ART
ADAM BROCKBANK

d|b
FICKLING
David Fickling Books
OXFORD · NEW YORK

MEZOLITH
A DAVID FICKLING BOOK 978 0 385 61826 7

First published thanks to the amazing DFC weekly comic,
May 2008 – March 2009 (Come back soon!!)

This edition published in Great Britain in 2010 by David Fickling Books,
a division of Random House Children's Books
A Random House Group Company

1 3 5 7 9 10 8 6 4 2

Text copyright © Ben Haggarty, 2010
Illustrations copyright © Adam Brockbank, 2010

The right of Ben Haggarty and Adam Brockbank to be identified as the
author and illustrator of this work has been asserted in accordance
with the Copyright, Designs and Patents Act 1988.

DAVID FICKLING BOOKS
31 Beaumont Street, Oxford, OX1 2NP

www.kidsatrandomhouse.co.uk
www.rbooks.co.uk

Addresses for companies within The Random House Group Limited
can be found at: www.randomhouse.co.uk/offices.htm

THE RANDOM HOUSE GROUP Limited Reg. No. 954009

A CIP catalogue record for this book is available
from the British Library.

Printed and bound in China

HEY! IMPUDENT BEE...

THE BEE IS FAST... BUT POIKA, *GREATEST-HUNTER-OF-ALL*, IS GAINING ON HIM...

SEE HOW *SILENT* HE IS...HOW *NIMBLE*, HOW *QUICK* AND *FEARLESS*.

11

12

THEY'RE GOING TO CALL THE BEAST, AND WHEN HE COMES, WE WANT HIM TO *FEAR* US.

WE LIE DOWN... WE WAIT... AND ON MY SIGNAL WE RISE AND *ROAR*.

GOOD, HE'S TAKEN THE BAIT. HE THINKS THERE'S A *COW* DOWN THERE.

STEADY, *SOTILAS*, STEADY.

NOW SOTILAS! GO!

13

17

BE STILL. EVERYONE SETTLE.

GREAT BULL, THE TIME OF LEAVING HAS COME. ULJAS, OUR LORD OF GAME, OUR MASTER OF PREY SUMMONED YOU TO US.

YOUR FLESH SHALL FEED; YOUR HIDE SHALL CLOTHE; YOUR FAT SHALL BURN IN OUR LAMPS.

GREAT BULL, SING A DEATH SONG. ACCEPT THAT THE WIND MUST RAISE YOUR SPIRIT, BEYOND SKY AND EARTH... TO THE WORLD OF FLOWERS, SWEET GRASS AND MORNING DEW.

THERE YOU WILL REST AND WANDER AT WILL...

UNTIL ULJAS CALLS YOU AGAIN TO OUR WORLD.

URGA

TATI, IS POIKA GOING TO *DIE?*

HE'S VERY WEAK. THE BULL WOUND WON'T HEAL. WE HAVE TO PREPARE OURSELVES FOR IT.

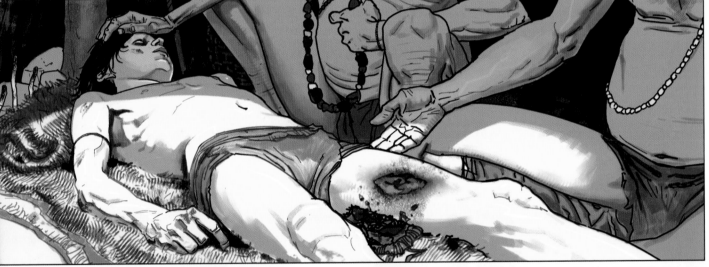

IT *STINKS* DOESN'T IT?

KORPPI VEHLO! YOU'VE COME FROM FAR AWAY. HOW DID YOU KNOW?

KORPPI VEHLO **SMELLED** IT. KORPPI VEHLO HAS BEEN WATCHING FOR A MONTH, SHE KNOWS EVERYTHING. AND SHE KNOWS THAT YOUR SON WILL SOON BE FLESH FOR CROWS...

...UNLESS YOU DO SOMETHING **NOW**.

SO... LET'S SEE WHAT KORPPI HAS IN HER **SPECIAL BAG**... SHE HAS...

...HERBS, TO BREAK THE FEVER.

...AND **FLY-WORMS** TO CLEAN THE WOUND.

AND YOU, **VANHA KONKARI**, TELL HIM THE STORY...

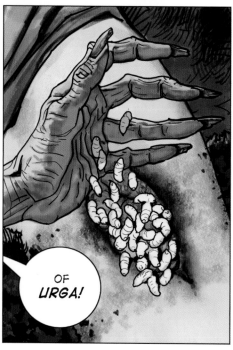

OF **URGA!**

VANHA, WHAT'S HAPPENING?

SHHH, LITTLE ONE, JUST LISTEN.

ONE MORNING...

AT THE TIME OF THE NUT MOON...

THREE BROTHERS...

...WENT *HUNTING*.

ALL DAY THEY STALKED A HEAVY STAG.

UNTIL...

25

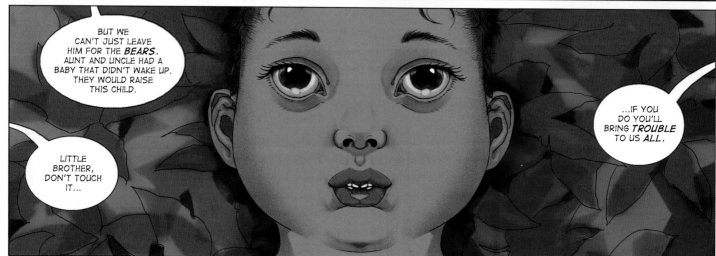

26

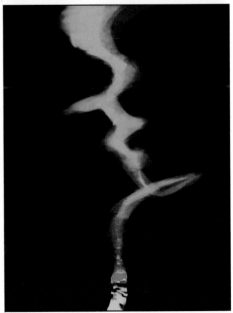

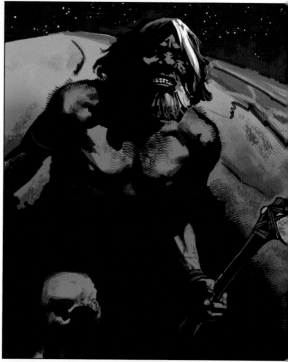

28

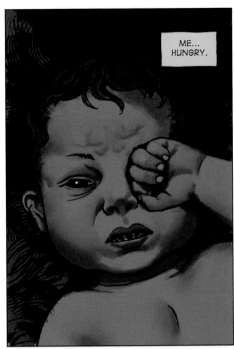

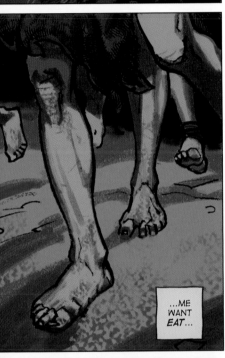

I DID IT! I DESTROYED HIM!

YOU PUT AN END TO THE TROUBLE...

...YOU PUT AN END TO URGA.

GOOD, THE FEVER'S BROKEN. IT WON'T BE LONG TILL WE CAN STITCH AND BIND THE WOUND AGAIN... AND THIS TIME IT WILL HEAL.

BUT, VANHA, THAT WASN'T THE END OF THE STORY WAS IT? WARN HIM.

YOU'RE RIGHT, KORPPI VEHLO. THIS STORY HAS NO END...

POIKA, AT THE HEART OF THE WORLD THERE IS A CAVE...

...AND IN THAT CAVE THERE ARE COUNTLESS URGAS, ALL SLEEPING... ALL DREAMING... AND WHEN ONE DREAMS THAT A BROTHER HAS BEEN DESTROYED...

...HE WAKES. CRAWLS INTO THE WORLD.

FINDS SOME HUMANS AND CRIES PITIFULLY NEAR THEM... UNTIL SOMEONE COMES TO CARE FOR HIM...

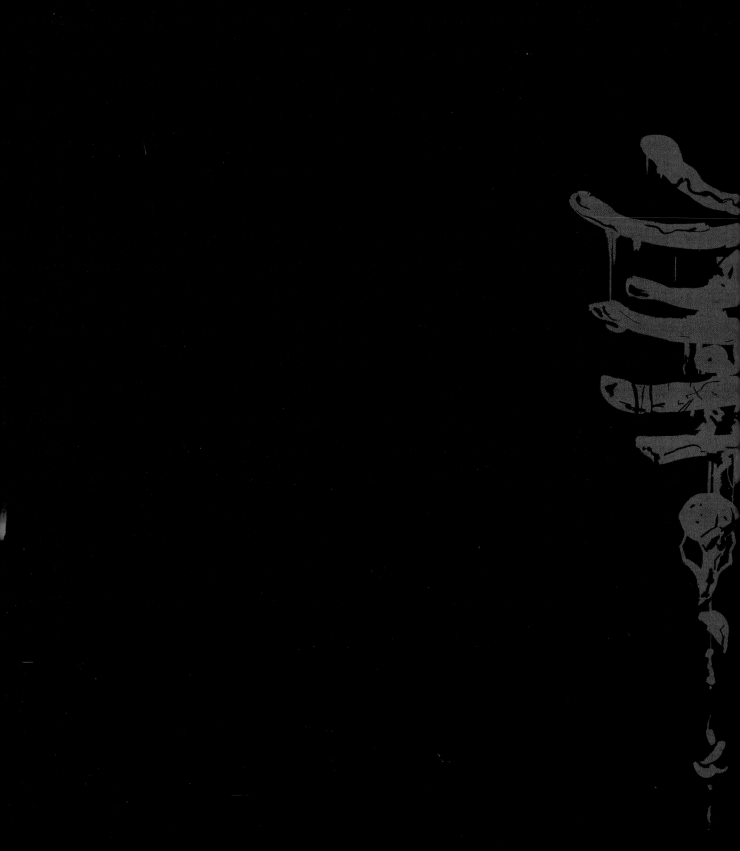

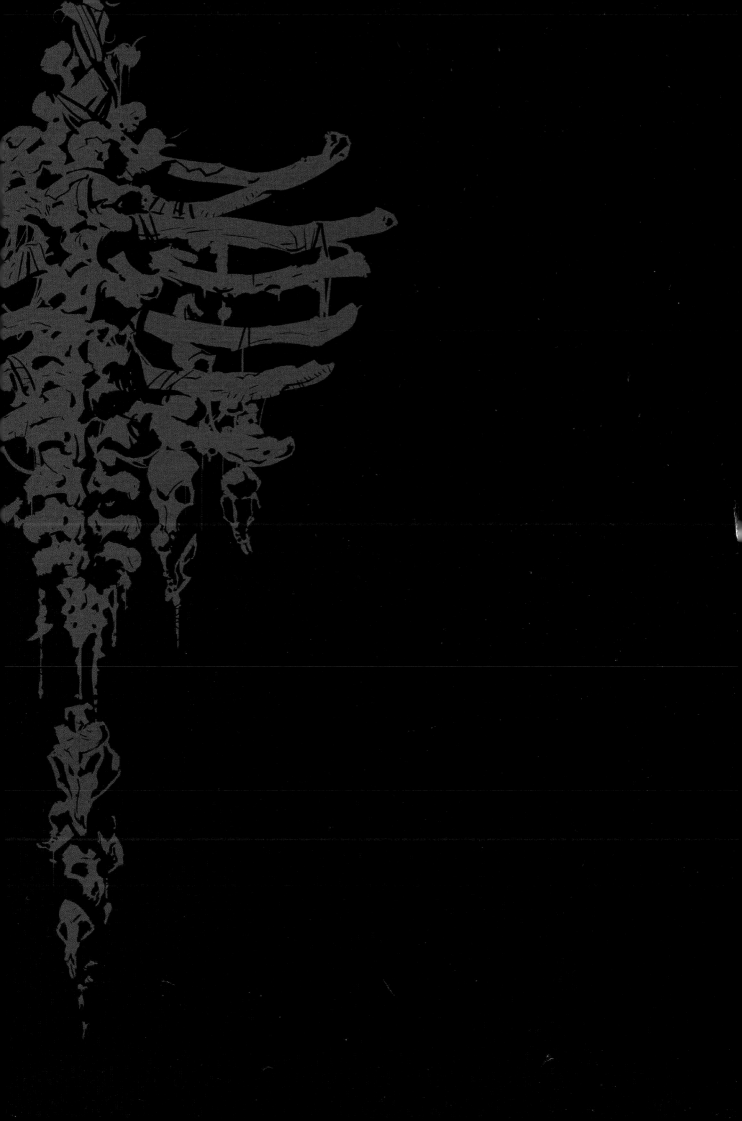

IT'S BEEN SO *HOT* THIS SUMMER THAT EVEN THE *SNAKE EGGS* ARE DRY!

TASTY THOUGH.

ARE YOU SURE YOUR *LEG* ISN'T HURTING TOO MUCH, POIKA?

NO, IT'S FINE... FIT AND WORKING.

WE SET MORE *TRAPS* UP THERE YESTERDAY...

LET'S GO.

YOU KNOW YOU REALLY SHOULDN'T BE HERE, POIKA.

PESTERING FATHER TO LET YOU COME LIKE THAT WAS *WRONG*.

... BUT *EKA*, THERE'S NOTHING TO DO BACK AT THE CAMP.

THIS IS *ONLY* TRAP SETTING. IT'S NOT AS IF IT'S A *BIG HUNT*.

TRAP SETTING IS NOT A GAME, IT'S *WORK*, AND YOU'RE PRETENDING TO BE BETTER.

WE CAN SEE YOU'RE STILL HURT...

... AND THIS WILL ONLY MAKE IT *WORSE*. YOU SHOULD BE RESTING.

THERE'S A GOOD FALLING TRAP ON THE *PIG PATH* OVER THE RIDGE.

MMM... *SWEET FAT MEAT!*

STRANGE STORM LAST NIGHT EH, *TOKA?* THUNDER... LIGHTNING...

...BUT NO *RAIN*.

THE *WIND* IS UP.

37

FIRE!

WE SHOULD GO BACK.

THE FIRE'S NOT COMING THIS WAY.

...AND WHAT ABOUT FAT *PIGGY?*

VERY WELL, BOYS. BUT WE MUST BE *QUICK*.

IT'S BEEN SPRUNG. PIGGY GOT THE BETTER OF THE TRAP... AND OUR *BELLIES* GOT THE BETTER OF US.

THIS IS GETTING *BAD*.

THE *WIND* IS CHANGING DIRECTION.

IT'S DRIVING THE FIRE *TOWARDS* US! IT'S TOO STRONG.

THAT COULD HAVE BEEN WORSE...

ROAST BIRDY, EKA?

BETTER ONE ROASTED BIRDY THAN THREE ROASTED *HUNTERS!*

MAKE THAT *FOUR* HUNTERS!

LOOK, FATHER, I'VE CAUGHT US A FI... WHAT'S THIS?

THIS, SON, IS THE *BOUNDARY*.

THIS IS NO PLACE FOR *OUR* PEOPLE. WE SHOULD GET BACK INTO THE WATER... THE RIVER BELONGS TO ALL...

OWL PEOPLE!

EMPTY YOUR HANDS!

SEIZE THEIR *CATCH*.

YOU KNOW THE *ORDER* OF THINGS. WE DO NOT INTRUDE ON YOUR *HUNTING GROUNDS* WITHOUT INVITATION ...AND YOU DO NOT INTRUDE ON OURS!

BUT WE WERE *CAUGHT*. WE HAD NO CHOICE.

AND NOW, *'LEFTHAND'* YOU'RE CAUGHT AGAIN. THE ORDER CANNOT BE BROKEN. WE OWLS MAKE *NO* EXCEPTIONS.

WE'LL LEAVE NOW... WADE DOWN-RIVER BACK TO OUR TERRITORY.

NO! NOT UNTIL YOU HAVE *BOUGHT* YOUR FREEDOM. WE'LL TAKE YOUR CATCH TO BEGIN WITH... BUT IT'S NOT *ENOUGH*.

...GIVE HIM BACK HIS BOW AND QUIVER.

42

WHY THE **SECOND** ARROW, 'LEFTHAND'?

BECAUSE IF I HAD KILLED MY OWN **SON**, I WOULD HAVE BURIED IT IN YOUR **HEART**.

THEN THERE WOULD HAVE BEEN A **GREAT MANY** DEATHS HERE... **SET THEM FREE!** GIVE THEM EVERYTHING BACK... EXCEPT THE CATCH. AND **YOU**, 'LEFTHAND'...

IF **EVER** YOU COME HERE AGAIN, YOU WILL **DIE**. ...AND IT WILL NOT BE QUICK.

44

SWAN
BRIDE

VANHA, WHY DOES TALJA THE CAMP-KEEPER ALWAYS LOOK SO OLD AND MISERABLE?

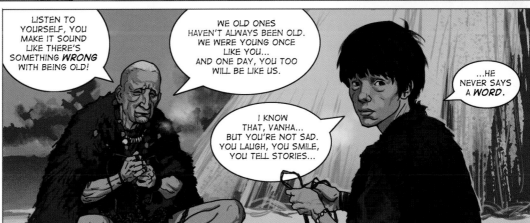

LISTEN TO YOURSELF, YOU MAKE IT SOUND LIKE THERE'S SOMETHING **WRONG** WITH BEING OLD!

WE OLD ONES HAVEN'T ALWAYS BEEN OLD. WE WERE YOUNG ONCE LIKE YOU... AND ONE DAY, YOU TOO WILL BE LIKE US.

I KNOW THAT, VANHA... BUT YOU'RE NOT SAD. YOU LAUGH, YOU SMILE, YOU TELL STORIES...

...HE NEVER SAYS A **WORD**.

TALJA HAS SEEN MORE THAN ANY OF US **KANSA PEOPLE**. THERE IS A REASON FOR HIS SORROW...

POIKA, DO YOU WANT TO HEAR A STORY?

YES, ALWAYS!

WELL...

THERE WAS ONCE A YOUNG HUNTER...

47

...WHO KNEW A GOOD PLACE TO *HUNT*.

ONE MORNING FIVE GREAT *SWANS* FLEW DOWN TO THE LAKE.

AND WHEN THEY TOUCHED THE WATER, THEY *CHANGED*...

48

IS *THIS* WHAT YOU'RE LOOKING FOR?

YES. *PLEASE* GIVE IT BACK. WITHOUT IT I *CANNOT* GET HOME.

NO, WOMAN, YOU'RE TOO BEAUTIFUL. *ULJAS* HAS BLESSED ME. I CANNOT ALLOW YOU TO LEAVE. TODAY I HAVE CAUGHT A VERY GREAT PRIZE. YOU ARE *MINE.*

MAN, I AM NOT *YOURS.* DO NOT *TOUCH* ME. IF YOU DO, I'LL DIE... I AM NOT FROM *YOUR* WORLD.

I COME FROM BEYOND THE PLACE WHERE THE SKY AND THE WATER MEET. THERE, WITH MY SISTERS WE LIVE *IMMORTAL.* IF I AM ONCE TOUCHED BY A MORTAL IN YOUR WORLD, THEN MORTALITY WILL PASS TO ME. *DEATH* WILL HAVE THE SAME POWER OVER ME THAT SHE HAS OVER YOU.

LET ME GO BACK WITH MY SISTERS. *PLEASE,* MAN, LET ME LIVE.

I SHALL NOT TOUCH YOU. BUT, AS LONG AS I HAVE YOUR *CLOAK,* YOU WILL STAY HERE WITH ME... AS MY *BRIDE.*

WEAR THIS.

AND YOU SWEAR YOU WILL NEVER TOUCH ME?

YES, I *SWEAR* THAT NOT EVEN MY FINGER WILL BRUSH AGAINST YOU. I'LL NOT HARM MY GIFT.

HE BROUGHT HER TO THE *WINTER CAMP*, BUT DID NOT TELL ANYONE WHO SHE WAS OR HOW SHE CAME TO BE WITH HIM...

EVERYONE MARVELLED AT HER... HER STRANGE WHITE SKIN... AND HER HAIR.

THE HUNTER FOUND A HIDING PLACE FOR THE CLOAK.

AND THEY LIVED TOGETHER THROUGH A LONG, LONG WINTER.

TELL ME MORE ABOUT YOUR HOME?

IT IS A PLACE OF *CALM*, THE BREEZE IS ALWAYS *WARM*, THE SUN NEVER *TOO* HOT, AND AT NIGHT THE MOON IS FOREVER THE *BRIGHT MOON* OF FLOWERS.

HE NEVER ONCE TOUCHED HER.

BUT THE MOON OF FLOWERS RETURNED, AND IT WAS TIME TO *LEAVE* THE WINTER CAMP.

THE YOUNG HUNTER WAS DISTRAUGHT. HE HAD FALLEN IN LOVE WITH A STRANGE WOMAN THAT HE COULD NEVER TAKE IN HIS ARMS AND NOW SHE WAS *GONE*.

HE LEFT THE *KANSA* PEOPLE BEHIND...

HE LEFT *KOTI* COUNTRY BEHIND...

HE WENT IN SEARCH OF THE SWAN MAIDEN. HE FOLLOWED THE PATHS OF THE *STONE TRADERS*, AND SOUGHT PERMISSION TO CROSS BOUNDARIES.

ALWAYS HE ASKED THE *SAME* QUESTION: ALWAYS HE GOT THE *SAME* ANSWER.

WHICH WAY DO THE *SWANS* FLY IN SPRING?

TOWARD THE *SETTING SUN*.

IF YOU TRAVEL FAR TO THE *WEST* OF THE WORLD, YOU COME TO THE *SEA*.

HE HUNTED A BEAST, SMOKED SOME OF THE MEAT, FILLED ITS BLADDER WITH WATER AND MADE A BOAT FROM ITS HIDE.

THEY AWOKE BY THE LAKE WHERE THE HUNTER HAD FIRST SEEN THE SWANS. THEY RETURNED TO THE WINTER CAMP. THEY WERE *WELCOMED* – AND THEY LIVED TOGETHER AS *MAN* AND *WIFE*.

BUT, *POIKA*, WITHIN A YEAR SHE BECAME PREGNANT... AND, LIKE YOUR MOTHER, SHE *DIED* IN CHILDBIRTH. IT WAS TRULY TERRIBLE: NOT ONLY THE MOTHER DIED BUT ALSO THE BABY *BOY*.

SO, *POIKA*, NOW YOU KNOW THE SORROWS THAT *TALJA* CARRIES IN HIS HEART.

THE HUNTER TOOK THE BODIES OF THE SWAN BRIDE AND THEIR CHILD TO A SMALL *ISLAND* IN THE EAST... AN ISLAND OVER WHICH, EACH DAY, THE *SUN* RISES.

HE BURIED THEM THERE. HE BURIED THEM WITH THE *SWAN FEATHER* CLOAK.

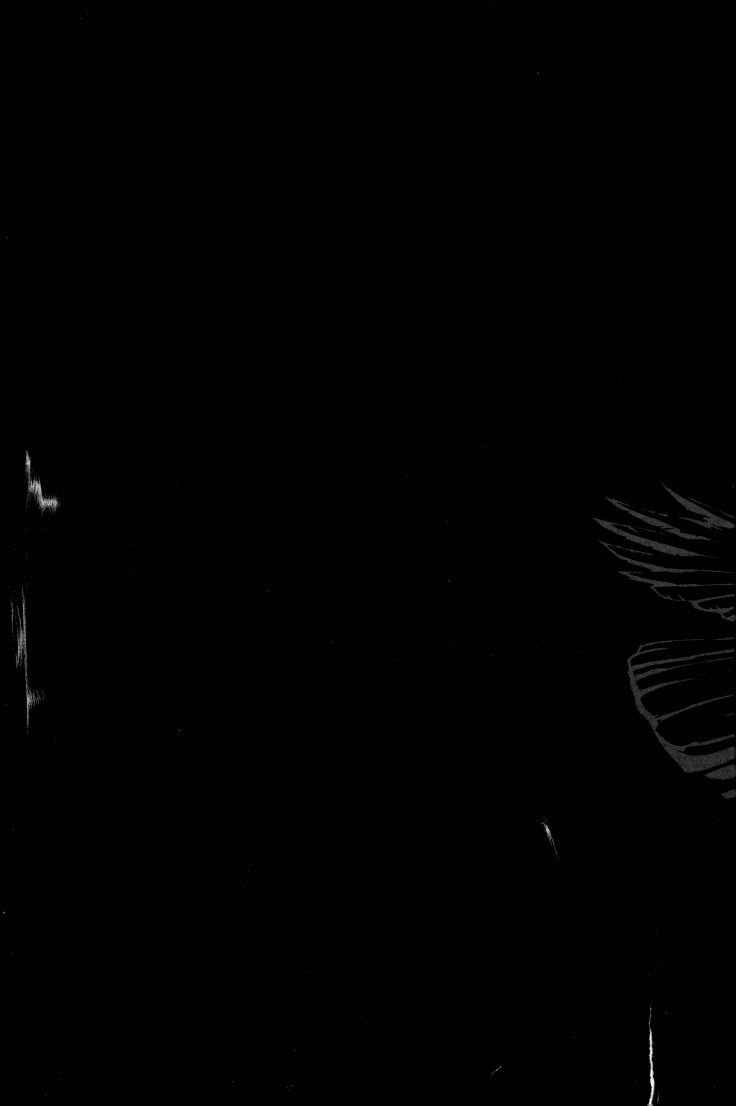

RAVEN

THAT'S IT FOR THIS YEAR. NOT SO MANY *NUTS* THIS TIME.

AND THEY'RE A BIT *HARD.*

IT WAS TOO *DRY* THIS SUMMER...

YES... THAT'S ABOUT ALL I'M *ALLOWED* TO DO! BUT IF *FATHER* WON'T TAKE ME HUNTING, AT LEAST I CAN BRING HIM SOME GOOD WOOD FOR *ARROW SHAFTS.*

...POIKA, HAVE YOU RESET THE *SQUIRREL* TRAPS?

BE CAREFUL, POIKA! WE HAVEN'T GOT A *FIRE POUCH:* WE CAN'T MAKE ANY SMOKE.

IT'LL BE FINE – THE BEES ARE DROWSY NOW. AND ANYWAY, THEY *LIKE* ME.

HEY! THERE'S A *BEE'S* NEST UP THERE!

I MIGHT NOT BE ABLE TO *RUN,* BUT I CAN STILL *CLIMB...* WE'LL BE SWEETENING NUTS WITH HONEY THIS WINTER!

ARE YOU *SURE?*

IN THE NAME OF *ULJAS,* WHAT IS *THAT?!*

YEEOW!!

OOOF!!

ARE YOU *ALRIGHT?*

JUST A BIT *BRUISED* – THE BRANCHES BROKE MY FALL – BUT WHAT WAS *THAT?* ON THE CRAGS, THE *HUGE BIRD!* IT SCARED ME.

YOU SHOULD BE ASKING *WHO* WAS THAT! YOU'VE MET HER BEFORE!

YOU WON'T REMEMBER, YOU WERE IN A *FEVER.*

HER? I'VE NEVER SEEN *HER* BEFORE.

SHE'S *KORPPI VELHO.* SHE'S *KANSA* BUT USUALLY SHE STAYS VERY FAR AWAY: WE CAN NEVER GO TO HER AND SHE SELDOM COMES TO US.

BUT WHEN YOU WERE SICK SHE DID COME. SHE CAME AND SAVED YOUR *LIFE...* AND NOW SHE'S SHOWN HERSELF TO YOU AGAIN.

I WONDER WHY...

YOU KNOW THAT CERTAIN BIRDS ARE *SACRED* TO US? LUCK BIRDS: HAWKS, SWANS, OWLS... RAVENS. WE, *KANSA* PEOPLE, DO NOT KILL THEM... BUT ONCE, ONE SPRING, A HUNTER BROUGHT DOWN A *RAVEN...*

HIS PREGNANT WIFE HAD CRAVED AND CRAVED *RAVEN FLESH* AND *RAVEN EGGS...*

THE MEAT AND EGGS WERE *BITTER* AND SHE GAVE BIRTH TWO MOONS TOO SOON...

DO YOU STILL HAVE THE RAVEN'S SKIN?

I'LL FETCH IT FOR YOU.

THE MIDWIFE *WRAPPED* THE CHILDS BODY IN THE RAVEN'S SKIN AND CARRIED IT INTO THE FOREST.

SHE PLACED THE BODY SOMEWHERE SAFE...

... A *NEST GRAVE* FOR THE CORPSE.

BY SITTING STILL AND ALLOWING THE FLIES TO CRAWL INTO HER MOUTH, THE BABY FED HERSELF... AND *GREW*.

ONE DAY, A WOMAN FORAGING...

...FOUND THE *RAVEN CHILD*.

SHE WAS TAKEN HOME, BUT SHE WOULDN'T EAT ANYTHING EXCEPT *CARRION*.

EVERYONE *FEARED* HER, BUT NO-ONE WOULD *HARM* HER: THEY SENSED HER *POWER*.

YOU PEOPLES IS NOT *MY* PEOPLES. *THESE* IS MY PEOPLES. KORPPI'S PEOPLE *FLY*...

ONE DAY THE BIRDS LED HER AWAY.

SOMEHOW SHE MADE HER *NEST* UP ON THAT CLIFF. SHE LIVES UP THERE... LIKE I SAID, WE NEVER GO TO HER... BUT SOMETIMES SHE *CHOOSES* TO COME TO US.

SHE *SAVED* YOU, POIKA...

MISSING

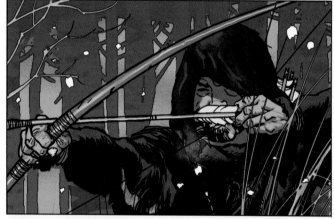

ACH! ULJAS DEMANDS WE MAKE A CLEAN KILL. HIS CREATURES SHOULD NOT SUFFER. I NEED TO CATCH AND SEND THIS SOUL QUICKLY.

FATHER'S BEEN MISSING *THREE* DAYS.

WHY ARE WE JUST *SITTING* HERE? WE SHOULD BE *OUT* SEARCHING FOR HIM.

PATIENCE, EKA. AS SOON AS THE STORM STOPS WE WILL GO, BUT UNTIL THEN, THERE IS NO POINT.

RATHER *ONE* MAN LOST, THAN *ALL*.

BUT *THREE DAYS*, VAHVA...

WHEN YOUR SON WENT MISSING THAT WINTER, IT WAS *TOO* LATE...

IT WAS.

YOU GOT US INTO THIS TROUBLE!

YOU'D BETTER GET US OUT OF IT!

NO! I DID NOT...

... I DID NOT!!

... I DID NOT GET US INTO THIS TROUBLE... BUT I WILL TRY TO GET US OUT OF IT.

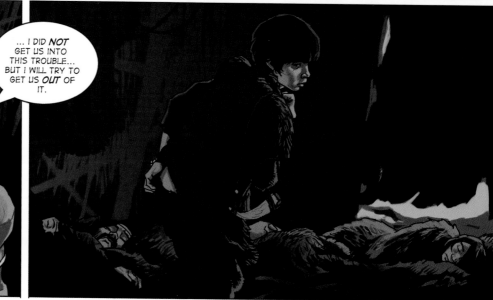

MY BEE
ISN'T HERE
TO HELP ME –
BUT THESE BEES
MIGHT...

WHO COMES TO SWEETEN *KORPPI'S* DRY OLD BEAK WITH HONEY?

I DO - BUT HOW DID YOU KNOW I HAD *HONEY?*

KORPPI VELHO KNOWS MANY THINGS.

KORPPI KNOWS YOU IS THE *LITTLEY* ONE WHO TRIES FLYING AND ALWAYS *FALLS*.

WHAT DO YOU *MEAN?*

FLIES ON *BULL HORNS*, FLIES INTO *RIVER*, FLIES DOWN *TREES*... LITTLEY ONE FLIES AND LITTLE SELF *HURTS*.

I DIDN'T *FLY* DOWN THIS CLIFF!

YES, IN *ICY* TIME TOO... FLEDGLING DID GOOD. *BRAVE*...

NOW, LITTLEY ONE SWEET FEED ME *HONEY* AND TELL ME WHY YOU COME?

FATHER WENT HUNTING ON HIS OWN...

IT *SNOWED*... AND HE HASN'T COME BACK.

DO YOU KNOW WHERE HE IS?

MMPH! NO. KORPPI NOT KNOW THAT.

KORPPI, WILL YOU COME AND *HELP* US?

YES- BUT *NO TELL OTHERS!*

74

WE SEARCHED FOR *TWO* DAYS. WE CAN'T FIND HIM.

WE DON'T EVEN KNOW WHICH *WAY* HE WENT.

HE LEFT NO SIGNALS, NO TRACES, NO MARKS?

NOTHING.

MUCH TOO MUCH *SNOW.*

CLIMBING BOY DID *KORPPI* CALL.

TIME IS GOOD. NOW *KORPPI* COMES TO HELP FIND *BOYFATHERMAN.* GIVE ME SOMETHING *HIS.*

BED BUNDLE *GOOD.*

HMMMM... BED BUNDLE FULL OF *MAN-STINK.*

KORPPI, DANCES NOW. KORPPI HOPS FOR CROW LORD.

BEAT MUSIC ON *STICKS,* BEAT MUSIC ON *BONES...*

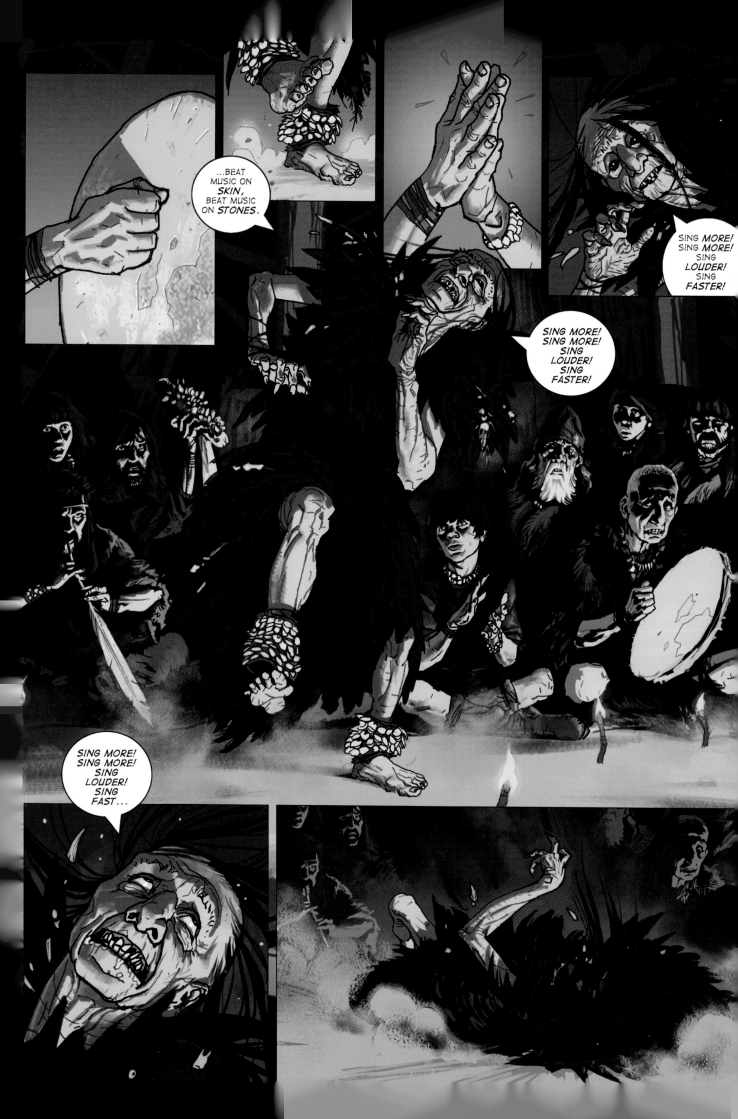

SHHHH...

WHERE ARE WE GOING?

THIS REALLY ISN'T GOOD. WE'RE FOLLOWING A *LAME BOY* AND A *RAGGED RAVEN* TO WHO KNOWS WHERE...

WE SHOULD HAVE OUR *SPEARS* AND *BOWS* WITH US. OR AT LEAST, *AXES!*

AND WHY THESE *SLOW, OLD MEN?*

EKA! TOKA! BE QUIET AND DO AS SHE SAYS!

THE *BOUNDARY!*

HMM! NOT SO 'LITTLE BROTHER'.

BUT YOUR *FATHER* WOULDN'T HAVE COME HERE? NOT AFTER THAT *NASTINESS* DURING THE *FAT MOON.*

IF *KORPPI* WANTS US TO CROSS THE BOUNDARY, WE *CROSS* THE BOUNDARY.

BUT IF WE MUST, THEN WE DO IT *QUIETLY.*

THERE HE IS.

IN THE NAME OF *ULJAS*, WHAT HAVE THEY *DONE* TO OUR FATHER?

INDEED, YES. THERE HE IS!

YOU *KANSA* HAVE COME *QUIETLY*, BUT WE *OWLS* GLIDE *SILENTLY*.

WELL NOW, HAVEN'T MY *CLEVER OWLS* CAUGHT ME A *TASTY MOUTHFUL OF MICE.*

IS HE DEAD?

NOT *YET*. REMEMBER THAT I PROMISED *LEFTHAND* THAT IF HE RETURNED, HE WOULD MEET A *SLOW DEATH*.

HO, *TURHA*, SHALL I FETCH HIS FATHER'S *BOW*?

AH, *YES!* THAT WOULD BE *FUN!* BRING ANOTHER *PINE FRUIT* AND WE'LL SEE WHAT *SKILLS LEFTHAND* TAUGHT HIS SON!

OH, *LEFTHAND*, GREAT HUNTER THAT YOU ARE, SING A *DEATH SONG*...

LOOK! ISN'T THAT OUR *TUTTA?* BESIDE THE CHILD WITH THE *MARK?*

IT IS, BUT SHE MARRIED A *LONG-SUMMER* MAN FOUR YEARS AGO. HOW DID SHE GET *HERE?*

THEY'RE *STARVING*.

STOP!

84

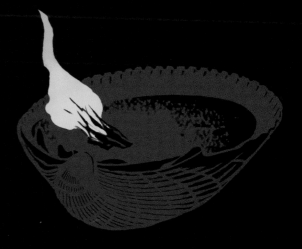

HANDS

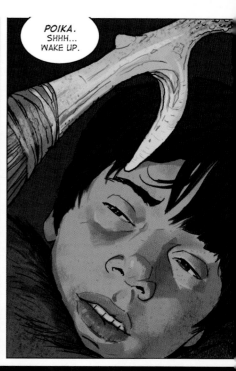

POIKA.
SHHH...
WAKE UP.

WHAT?
WHY?

SHH.
TODAY IS A
SPECIAL DAY FOR
YOU. DON'T ASK
ANY QUESTIONS.

YOU'LL
NEED THESE.
AND BRING
YOUR *STICK.*

THIS WILL
MAKE A *LIGHT*
TO HELP YOU
FIND YOUR
WAY.

AND THIS
WILL MAKE
YOU A *PATH*
TO FOLLOW
BACK.

WHA...?

SHHH. **GO IN THERE.** AS **FAR** AS YOU CAN MANAGE.

KIVA HAS MADE A VERY **LONG ROPE** FOR YOU. THEN YOU'LL FIND WHAT YOU'LL FIND... I THINK YOU'LL UNDERSTAND WHAT NEEDS TO BE DONE.

REMEMBER, I AM AT THE OTHER END OF THIS, WAITING FOR YOU.

I THINK BEE JUST KISSED ME!

YES, SON. I THINK HE DID.

More stories from

The DFC Library

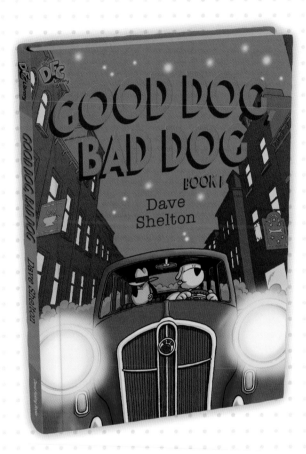

THE SPIDER MOON:

In a world on the brink of destruction, how will Bekka cope with the journey ahead?

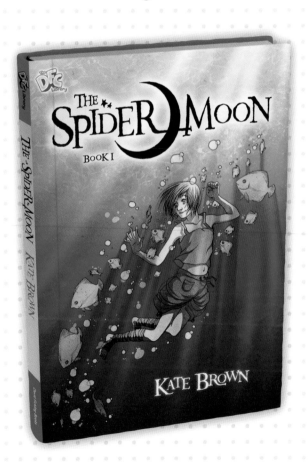

GOOD DOG, BAD DOG:

Canine crooks will have to watch their tails as doggy detectives, Bergman and McBoo, sniff out crime.

Collect them all!